Dinosaurs in a line

Which dinosaur is number one in the line? Which is first? Which is number two or second?

Children draw lines to match the numeral 1 to the first dinosaur, 2 to the second dinosaur, etc.

Count along the line to the fourth dinosaur. Which is the next dinosaur? Count on to the seventh. Which is next?

Name that dinosaur

Velociraptor

Apatosaurus

Diplodocus

Stegosaurus

Pterodactyl

Scelidosaurus

Triceratops

Tyrannosaurus Rex

Point to a dinosaur. *What is this dinosaur's name?* Read the names. Encourage children to find names of dinosaurs they know or use a reference book.

Help children to read each name using clues such as the initial letter. Children colour the name in the same colour as the dinosaur.

Children name some dinosaurs not on the page and describe them to you.

Abacus *evolve*

F

I Can Do...
Book I

Ginn

Dinosaur facts

All dinosaurs ate meat. ☐

Some dinosaurs could fly. ☐

Dinosaurs are extinct. ☐

All dinosaurs were very big. ☐

Dinosaurs had five legs. ☐

Some dinosaurs could run. ☐

What do we know about dinosaurs? Do all dinosaurs eat meat? Do some eat plants? Are there dinosaurs around nowadays?

Children read the statements with help, then write T beside the statements they agree to be true, and F beside those they agree to be false.

Can children make their own factual statements about dinosaurs?

My footprint

My foot is ☐ cubes long

How long is your foot? How many cubes do you think will fit along it? Is it longer or shorter than your hand?

Children draw carefully round their socked foot in the space provided and lay cubes along their drawing to see how many cubes long it is.

Children look around and find things that are longer/ shorter than their foot, e.g. ruler = longer, crayon = shorter, etc.

3

What are dinosaurs like?

as long as

_____

as fast as

_____

as spiky as

_____

as fierce as

_____

  Point to the first dinosaur and its simile. *What is really long? What can we compare this dinosaur to?* E.g. a train, a road.

Children write an appropriate simile, either independently or with your help in the space provided.

Can children invent their own similes about dinosaurs?

How many dinosaurs?

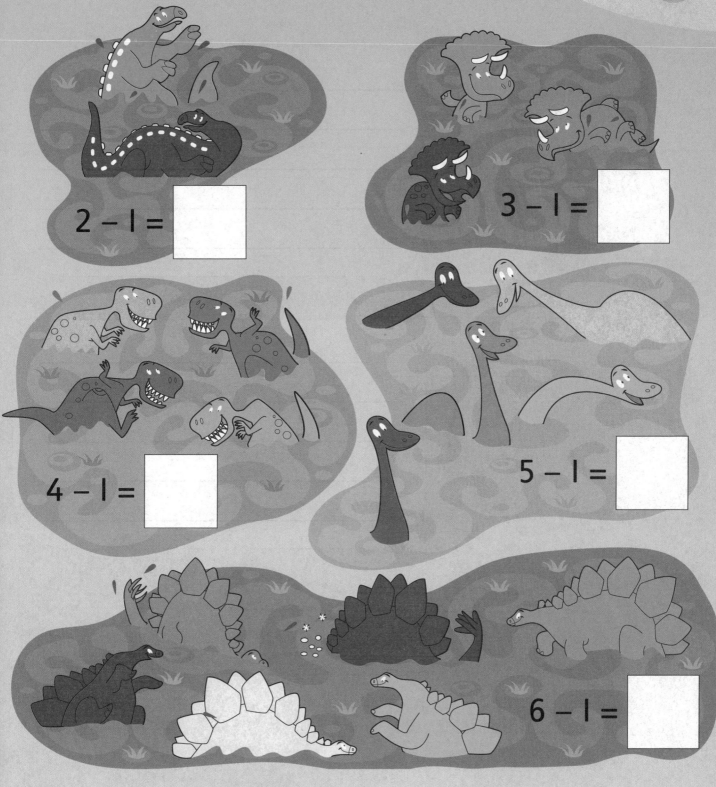

$2 - 1 =$

$3 - 1 =$

$4 - 1 =$

$5 - 1 =$

$6 - 1 =$

How many dinosaurs in this swamp? If one leaves (cross it out), how many are left in the swamp? Repeat for each swamp.

Children write the number of dinosaurs left when one leaves the swamp, or they tell you the number and you write it for them.

How many dinosaurs will be left here if two leave the swamp?

Talking to a dinosaur

 Think about the talk that the man and the dinosaur had at the end of Dinosaurs and all that Rubbish. *What should this man and dinosaur say?*

Children dictate some words for you to write in the speech bubbles or write some words themselves.

Can children extend the conversation? *How cross might the dinosaur be? What could the man say back?*

What shapes can you see?

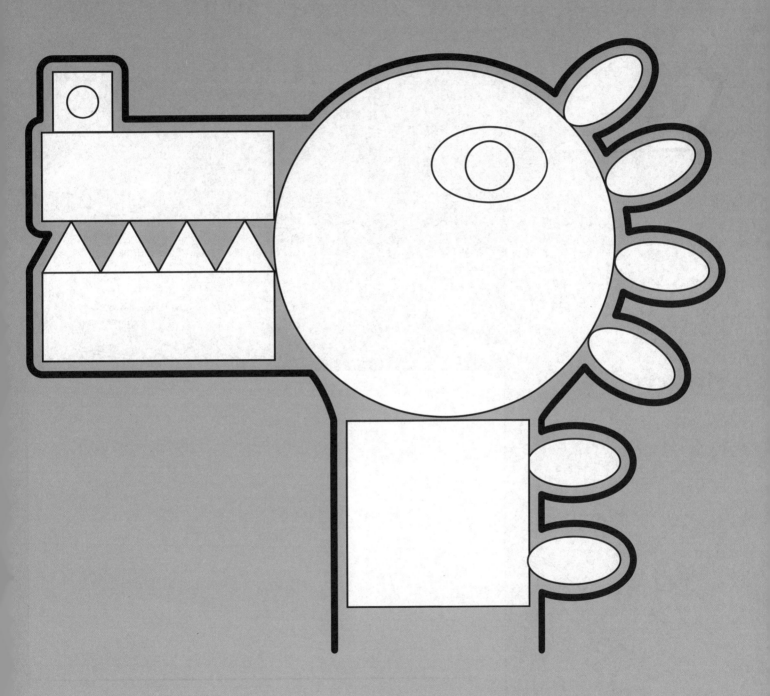

Can we see any triangles on the dinosaur's head? Can we see any squares? Circles? Oblongs?

Children colour squares in orange, circles in yellow, triangles in red, and oblongs in blue. Other shapes can be any colour they choose.

Can children arrange 2D (flat) shapes to create their own dinosaur?

Action words

sleep

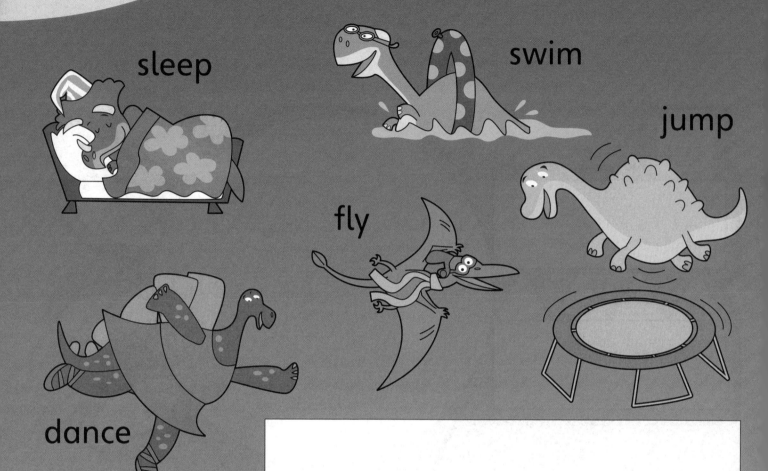

swim

jump

fly

dance

tiptoe

Point at a dinosaur and its action word. Read the word together. Ask children to perform this action!

Children write their own action word in the space and draw a dinosaur performing their action.

Can children think of some more dinosaur actions e.g. run, climb, slither?

Counting dinosaurs

$$4 + 2 = 6$$

$$5 + 1 = 6$$

$$3 + 3 = 6$$

Point at a lake. *How many green dinosaurs are there? How many red dinosaurs? How many dinosaurs in the lake?* Find the matching addition.

Children draw lines to match each lake to an appropriate number sentence.

Can children think of a lake that has six dinosaurs in it and is not on this page (e.g. six green dinosaurs and no red ones to match 6 + 0 = 6?

Pages I have

Week 11

Week 12

Week 13

Week 14

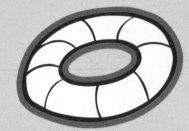

Week 15

Week 16

Week 17

Week 18

Week 19

Week 20

enjoyed doing

Week 11

Week 12

Week 13

Week 14

Week 15

Week 16

Week 17

Week 18

Week 19

Week 20

Think of some words

mum

dad

bib

nan

pip

pup

Sound out the words on the page with children, pointing at each letter and then blending to make the whole word.

Children write their own CVC words with the same start and end letter – these can be nonsense words!

Can children think of more words? Help them to write these.

Writing numbers

Discuss how we write each numeral. Practise forming each numeral by 'writing' with a finger on the table. Children do this before putting pen to paper.

Children write the appropriate numerals in the squares provided. They can practise their number formation in the large box.

Can children write numerals 5 and 6? Can they write a numeral with an appropriate number of objects to match?

15

Bedtime

What do we say at bedtime? What would you say if you put someone to bed? Be aware of children that do not speak English at home.

Children write their own bedtime words with help in spelling them.

Can children mind map words we say to wake someone up e.g. *wakey-wakey*?

Where is it?

under

in

left

beside

above

in front

over

out

right

on

below

behind

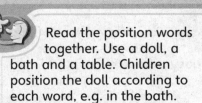

Read the position words together. Use a doll, a bath and a table. Children position the doll according to each word, e.g. in the bath.

Children join the appropriate position words to each toy to indicate its position in relation to the table.

Can children think of other position words? E.g. alongside, beyond etc.

Baby animals

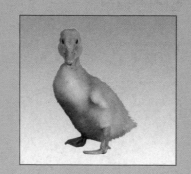

lamb

duckling

kitten

seal pup

Which baby animal goes with the seal? What do we call a baby seal? What do we call a baby cat?

Children draw lines between each animal and its baby. They then draw lines linking the baby animals to their names.

Can children think of the names of some other baby animals?

More or less?

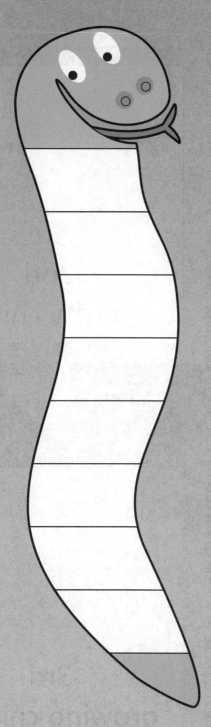

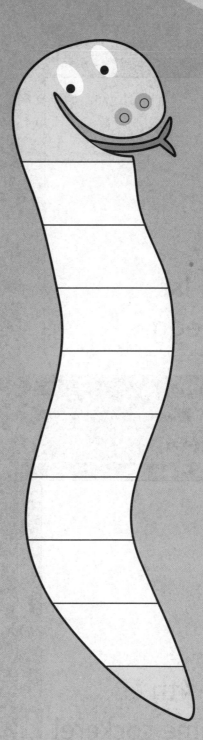

less than 3   more than 3

Children throw a dice. They look at the number thrown and decide if it is less than or more than 3.

Throw a dice. If the number is less than 3, children colour a part of the green snake. If it is more than 3, colour a part of the yellow snake.

Can children sort number cards 1–20 into those that are less than 10 and those that are more than 10?

Growing up

1st egg	2nd fluffy chick
4th handsome cockerel	3rd growing chicken

Discuss the stages from egg to cockerel. Help children with reading the captions.

Children draw pictures in each box to create a flow chart.

What are the stages that a human goes through from a baby to an adult? Can children draw a flow chart of these stages?

Heavier than me

Which things do you think are heavier than you? Which are lighter?

Children draw a cross by each photo of an object or an animal that they think is heavier than them.

Can children name some objects or animals which they think might be the same weight as they are?

Scary animals

Discuss the creatures on the page. *Would these be scary to the baby owls? Would they scare us?* What other words do children know for scared?

Children draw a cross next to the creatures that they think are scary.

Can children mind map some more scary creatures that are awake at night?

Night animals

owl

sheep

chicken

bat

dog

cow

fox

badger

pig

hedgehog

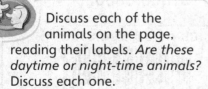
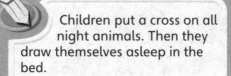
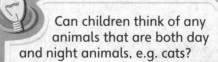

Discuss each of the animals on the page, reading their labels. *Are these daytime or night-time animals? Discuss each one.*

Children put a cross on all night animals. Then they draw themselves asleep in the bed.

Can children think of any animals that are both day and night animals, e.g. cats?

23

Abacus Evolve Foundation is the flexible literacy and mathematics programme for creative teaching and active learning that has practical planning and support for the *real* classroom at its heart.

The activities in this book are intended to be carried out in small groups with adult supervision. At the foot of each page, there are three types of instruction:

 Use the page as a stimulating and engaging resource to support discussion.

 Use the page as a record of understanding and achievement.

 Use the page as a starting point for ideas to extend and challenge children.

Also in *Abacus Evolve Foundation*:

Teacher Toolkit	978-0-602-57419-2
Photocopy Masters	978-0-602-57421-5
I Can Do Book 2 (pack of 8)	978-0-602-57425-3
F1 Big Book Pack	978-0-602-57426-0
F2 Big Book Pack	978-0-602-57427-7

Typeset by **Artistix**
Original illustrations © Pearson Education Ltd
Illustrated by **Viktoria Astrom, Volker Beisler, Matt Buckley, Seb Burnett, John Haslam, Darren Lingard, Andrew Painter, Anthony Rule** and **Jackie Stafford**
Cover illustration by **Per José Karlén**
Printed in Britain by **Ashford Colour Press**

Ginn is an imprint of Pearson Education Limited, a company incorporated in England and Wales, having its registered office at Edinburgh Gate, Harlow, Essex, CM20 2JE. Registered company number: 872828
www.ginn.co.uk
Ginn is a registered trademark of Pearson Education Limited

Text © Pearson Education Ltd 2008
First published 2008

12 11 10 09 08
10 9 8 7 6 5 4 3 2 1

British Library Cataloguing in Publication Data
A catalogue record for this book is available from the British Library

ISBN 978-0-602-57424-6 (pack of 8)

Acknowledgements
The author and publisher would like to thank the following individuals and organisations for permission to reproduce photographs:
© Alamy / Arco Images, hedgehog, p23; © Alamy / Philip Mugridge, badger, p23; © Comstock Images, bed, p21; © Corbis, cow, p23; © Corbis / Joe McDonald, bat, p23; © Creatas, fox, p23; © Digital Stock, owl, p23 and seal pup, p18; © Digital Vision, elephant, p21; © Dreamstime / Midhat Becar, tyrannosaurus rex, p4 and p5; © Dreamstime / Ron Chapple Studios, diplodocus, p4 and p5; © Getty Images / PhotoDisc, cat, kitten, lamb, duck and duckling, p18, cat, p21 and dog, p23; © Guillaume Dargaud, seal, p18; © Jupiter Images / Photos.com, pterodactyl, p4 and p5 and car, p21; © Pearson Education Ltd / Ben Nicholson, p17; © Pearson Education Ltd / Tudor Photography, apatosaurus, p2 and p5, diplodocus, p2, triceratops, p2 and p5, scelidosaurus, p2 and p5, velociraptor, p5, sheep, p18, scooter, p21, sheep and chicken, p23; © Reed International Books, Australia PTY / Mario Borg, teddy, p21; © Shutterstock / RICKT, stegosaurus, p4 and p5; © Shutterstock / Walter Quirtmair, pig, p23.

Every effort has been made to contact copyright holders of material reproduced in this book. Any omissions will be rectified in subsequent printings if notice is given to the publishers.

Abacus Evolve

To find out more about Ginn products, plus free supporting resources, visit

www.ginn.co.uk
01865 888020

ISBN 978-0-602-57411-6
9 780602 574116